ELASTIC STEEL

METHOD OF ATHLETIC CONDITIONING

The Power of One

Paul Zaichik

in collaboration with

BodyWeightCulture

www.ElasticSteel.net
Www.PaulZaichik.com
www.BodyWeightCulture.com
www.BWCulture.net

DISCLAIMER

This manual presents information based upon the research and personal experiences of the author. It is not intended to be a substitute for a professional consultation with a physician or other healthcare provider. Neither the publisher not the authors can be held responsible for any adverse effects or consequences resulting from the use of any of the information in this manual. They cannot be held responsible for any errors or omissions in the manual. If you have a condition that required medical advice, the publisher and author urge you to consult a competent healthcare professional. Please consult your physician or other healthcare professionals for all personal health problems, and also before starting a new physical fitness program. No health information in this manual should be used to diagnose, treat, cure or prevent any medical condition. Anyone who has been inactive for several years and is over 35 years of age, should consider seeing a physician before any exercise program. Any application of the recommendations set forth in the following pages is at the reader's discretion and sole risk. Once again please note that the author and publisher of this book are NOT RESPONSIBLE in any manner whatsoever for any injury that may result from practicing the techniques and/or following the instructions given within. Since the physical activities described herein may be too strenuous in nature for some readers to engage in safely, it is essential that a physician be consulted prior to training.

Written by: Paul Zaichik
Cover by: Robyn Cook
Photography by: Matthew Hanlon
Exercises are performed by:
Paul Zaichik, Lee Van Crause, Ronald Lee.

ISBN # 978-1-4276-2478-9

ABOUT THE AUTHOR

Paul Zaichik is an exercise science expert. His specialty is flexibility training as well as bodyweight conditioning. His innovative method is designed to have a maximum carry over into specific athletic techniques.

A large part of his talent is to assess an athlete and quickly understand what kind of training is needed for optimal techniques. Paul is the author of Books and DVD's on the topic of flexibility, martial arts and bodyweight training.

Over the years, Paul Zaichik has worked with a variety of individuals including athletes, entertainers, and military personnel. His ElasticSteel Method of Athletic Conditioning programs are used world wide by both professional and amateurs with great success.

ABOUT BODYWEIGHTCULTURE

BodyWeightCulture.com was created by a group of fitness, health and nutrition experts. Ready to land a helping hand whenever you have a question on how to better your body. It is a site developed for sharing tried and tested methods of bodyweight resistance routines and exercises free of charge! And for participants to share their knowledge, expertise and experiences with others, through our extensive forum, and everyday people publishing their own body weight exercises for the community to utilize, all free of charge!

Visit www.BodyWeightCulture.com for hundreds of free bodyweight exercises, routines, workouts, videos, contests and much more.

TABLE OF CONTENT:

INTRODUCTION
SECTION 1

Without further ado, lets get right into it: A functionality of one side training is rarely understood or practiced. Functional training is a specific preparation that matches as closely as possible the target task. Most athletes develop their strength with equal, two side techniques such as bench press, shoulder press, lat pull down, squat, etc. All of these techniques place near equal demand on the left and right side of the body. In most cases, the utilization of lateral or rotational stabilizers is minimal.

Let's examine a typical bilateral exercise, the bench press. When a bar is pressed in the air, the force is applied vertically and somewhat upward from the sternum toward the arm length over the shoulder level. Primary movers are flexors and horizontal flexors of the shoulder and extensors of the elbow. The stabilizers working here are primarily flexors and the extensors of the shoulder. Those prevent the arm from dropping the weight either in the direction of the lower body or over the head. In other words, the deltoids and somewhat biceps stabilize the bar upward preventing it from falling below the breast bone.

The lats, triceps, teres major and abdominals stabilize the bar from falling behind the head of the person. In real life it's more complicated, but for our purposes this basic conceptual explanation will do. What is lacking here is the lateral stabilizers. In other words, the bar will not fall left or right. The only way this will happen if there is more weight loaded on one side than another.

If you need further proof, think of a 100 lbs bench press. If someone presses a 100 lbs barbell, it will certainly be easier than two 50 lbs barbells. The reason for that is more stabilization is needed. In case of dumbbells, the chest and anterior deltoid must now stabilize to prevent the arms from flying outward. The triceps and posterior deltoid must stabilize the arm to prevent it from flying inward. Interesting, eh?

And we didn't even touch the most stabilizing challenge of all. Unilateral movement such as one, 50 lb dumbbell press, at a time. In other words, what is the difference between doing a bench press with 50 lbs in each hand compared to 50lbs in only one hand, while the other arm does nothing? The answer to that is - more stabilization is needed. In this case it's not the arms that carry the extra stabilization, but mostly the torso and even legs. So at this point, you can't argue that a 100 lb dumbbell with both hands, will work and develop the body differently than 50 lbs in one hand.

The next question is; As an athlete or a person who does function work, such as shoveling snow, lifting boxes, fixing cars; which type of training is more important? The answer to this question can be answered with another question. How often do you shovel with both arms and legs performing equal tasks? If you are an athlete how often do you throw, punch, catch, swing, kick, with both limbs doing the same and equal work. Let's say, with the exception of a few sports and activities, not very often, almost never. In that case, why train the strength that will not have the greatest carryover into your activity. Let's get something straight, "bilateral" strength training is better than no training at all, but not as good as unilateral, specific training.

This book deals with bodyweight training. However, there was a specific reason why the book began with the discussion of a classic power lifting technique. The point here is to avoid the assumption that the only reason to practice unilateral bodyweight training is because the bilateral training is too easy and the only way to increase resistance is to go unilateral. It's true that any time you switch to "one arming or one legging" the resistance multiplies, stabilizers get activated, muscle groups are engaged in a challenging, new dimensions. Yet, there is more than that. Building on the previous example we can say that the functionality of unilateral training is the main reason why it should be thought over the bilateral training, when the goal is the carry over into specific skills.

Right off the bat, an important question should be addressed. A question that is most likely looming in your mind. If unilateral training is so great, is there a reason to train bilateral. If it is so, then why, where and when? The answer is yes, bilateral exercises have their place. In many cases bilateral exercises are a preparation for the unilateral exercises. Think about it.

If you can't do one regular push up, how will you do a single arm pushup? Two limb exercises are also good endurance exercises, especially after the single limb exercises are mastered. They are also good, back-off routine exercises for unilateral practitioner.

There is another reason to do bilateral movement. It's important to understand that some exercises can't be done unilaterally. For example, a Body Press, or a Rocket are great maximum resistance exercises, which simply can be executed with one arm. (See Gravity Advantage Max Book for more details about these maximum resistance techniques.) As you can see, bilateral exercises have their place as well. Just keep in mind that unless your target skills call to kick with both legs at the same time or throw two balls with both hands at the same time, unilateral training should be included in your training regiment.

The exercises in this book are divided into two primary sections. Upper body and the lower body combined with midsection. It's important to understand that every unilateral upper body exercise will seek the stability from the mid-section muscles also. The upper body section has the exercises arranged in opposites. Most gravity advantage programs pair up the exercises that are opposite of each other. For example, pushups and rows, pull ups and shoulder presses and so on. It is advised to train the antagonists together if the skill and the technique availability allows it.

On the other hand, if you lack strength to work the opposing movement or no opponent exercise is present, then the closest substitution will do. For instance, if push-ups are performed, but you are not strong enough to do the rows as the pushup antagonist, you can do bent leg rows. Same applies to exercises that lack an exact antagonist. For example, one leg dead-lift doesn't have a direct antagonist, so an alternative exercise can be found to train the muscles that oppose the dead-lift movers.

In this book you will first learn a bilateral exercise, then it's powerful, functional cousin. Most exercises have a standard progression from two limbs to one limb. This method is described below. In some cases, a special exercise can serve as transition. If that's the case those will be mentioned as well.

SECTION I
CHAPTER 1 - The Standard Protocol

This is a time tested way to convert your two sided move into the Power of One. Before getting into it, though, let's just say the transition is not always easy and often takes patience. As long as you keep training carefully, your body will keep adapting and one day your desired skill will shine through. With that said, let's begin to understand the basic Power of One protocol.

Step 1
The Bilateral Skill

The first thing you need to do is to master the bilateral skill. We will take chin-ups as an example, but any other technique can be substituted here. A rule of thumb is number 20. You should be able to do 20 chin-ups prior to moving further. That's 20 close grip and 20 shoulder width grip. Wide grip at least 15.

Contra-Lateral Core training is part of any Gravity Advantage unilateral technique development. CLC exercises should be practiced toward the end of every ste's training session, as they prepare the core stabilizers for the challenge of supporting the unilateral movement. These exercises will be demonstrated as part of each section in the next paragraph.

Step 2
Weight or Resisted Closed Grip Training

This is a step where you add extra resistance to your close grip chin ups. Best bilateral to unilateral technique transfer is when close grip two arm movement is trained. This has to do with the fact that unilateral exercise must hold the base of support (hand, foot) over or under the center of gravity (center of the body) to maintain balance.

For example, when you do one leg squat, the standing leg must be under the center of the body, which is best simulated bilaterally when feet are together.

The resistance can be provided, using a weight vest, a back pack, a resistance band, a partner resistance or any other heavy object or means of adding opposition to the desired line of force. It is desirable to add at least one half of your body weight to normal resistance prior to moving on to the next part. In case of push-ups or rows, 35-40% of total bodyweight in addition to your own resistance should be quested.

Real weight, such as weight vest often works best. There are two reasons for that.

1. The real weight is measurable. For example, most weighted vests have increments. Partner resistance on the other hand is not reliably the same.
2. Real weight resistance doesn't change throughout the exercise. Elastic resistance on the other hand increases as the resistance band or tube gets more stretched.

Step 3
Unilateral Assisted Training

This is the first time you will be shifting the maximum focus to one arm. So start by getting a comfortable one arm grip on the bar. A thinner bar is usually easier to hold on to than a thicker bar. Gloves may help to prevent calluses, but may decrease the grip endurance. For assistance, you can use the commercial chin-up assistance machine, a partner or a resistance band held by the non-chinning arm. If nothing else is available, a rope can also be used to hold on to with the non-chining arm. The chin-up assistance machine or the resistance bands are usually the best choices. The main reason for that is assistance level adjustment capability. You can easily adjust the amount of weight that is lifting your body on the assistance machine. With a resistance band, the lower you hold it the less assistance it gives you. It's imperative to slowly bring the resistance down to the bare minimum in each training session.

For example, while on the chin-up assistance machine, start with 50 lbs of assistance. Let's assume you can do 6 reps with 50 lbs. Do 5 reps with each arm. Do not go to failure. After completing the set with each arm, rest for a minute or so. Come back and adjust the weights to 45 lbs. Now you can do 4 chin-ups with each arm. Do 3 repetitions and rest for a minute or so.

The next increment is 40 lbs and you find that you can do only 2 repetitions. Do one with each hand and rest. At the increment of 35lbs you can only do one. At this point do one with each arm and take a break. Come back to one more single rep set and then cool down.

Suggestion:

- You should do this no more than three times a week. However in case you are not sore the next day and it's been like that for two weeks, you can add a second training session to the same day. If you choose to add a second workout, you should remove the one rep set from the routine above. (In the example above this is the repetition with 35lbs of assistance)

The second session should be separated from the first one by at least one meal. For example, you have worked out from 11:00 to 11:45. At 12:30 you ate. At any point after 2 pm you can do another session. Depending on your digestion and metabolism level, you may have to eat a snack if you haven't eaten long after 12:30 meal. Regardless make sure that you have eaten between the two workouts and preferably will eat after the second workout. Training late at night is not recommended. If you do and are very hungry have only a modest meal after the evening session.

Your second chining session should be a different step three technique than the one used earlier during the day. For example if you used a chin-up assistance machine during your first session, you can use a rope, a partner or a resistance band as assistance. A single hand lat pull down on a lat pull down machine is also an option. Watch your body carefully, stop the session at the slightest sign of injury-like discomfort.

Regardless which method you choose if this is a grip mandated skill, such as a chin-up or a row an additional requirement calls for 15-20 second one arm dead-hang prior to completing this step. The grip training should be the last part of step three training.

Step 4
Eccentric Training

Old timers call this simply "Negatives". There are two main ways to do negative chin-ups. First is to pull yourself up with both hands close to each other and then to let go with one hand. The gravity will pull you down. You should fight it and come down as slow as possible.

If you'd like to play around with this you can do the chin up with one hand on the bar and the other hand holding the wrist of the first hand. You can then let go of the wrist and do the negative.

The lower on the forearm you hold with the supporting hand the more difficult the ascending becomes. Negative movements also get a bit more difficult this way because more effort was used on the concentric part of the technique. The second option is to jump up to the bar, holding only with one hand the whole time. If the bar is low enough for you to grasp with one hand, you may want to try this option. In case you can't control the negative movement at all and keep descending as fast as if you were holding on to nothing at all, this can only mean one thing. You have moved on to step four too soon. You should go back to step three and master it first.

The goal of step four is to come down in slow controlled movement, pausing every 20-30 degrees of elbow flexion. The slower you come down the closer you are to the one arm chin up.

Step 5
An unassisted negative and assisted positive movement.

For chin ups, a resistance band hanging along side your non-chining arm can be your final key to the one arm chin-up mastery. To do this you would grab the bar with your chining arm and the resistance band with a non-chining arm. Use the non-chining arm as a guide and pull yourself up, utilizing the strength of the chining arm as much as possible. When your elbow is completely flexed, let go off the resistance band. Come down as slowly as possible. At this point you may repeat the exercise without your feet having touched the ground. If that is too challenging at the moment, let go of the bar, stand on your feet, walk around for a minute and try again. As simple as it sounds, don't forget to do both arms.

The five steps outlined above is the back bone of unilateral training. If you choose to skip a step or add steps that's solely up to you. Skipping steps is another alternative to the Power of One transfer program. It is possible to achieve the one arm chin-up while skipping step two through four. This is not very scientific or safe, but it can be done and there's no point of denying it. If you can do 20 chin-ups, and then decide to rush into negatives, that is your choice. There is a chance that you will avoid injury and be successful. But doing so, brings a greater possibility that you will injure yourself, and thus, not achieve your goal as quickly as you could have, or even at all, due to injury.

Every transition will be demonstrated as described above. In the following chapters of the book there will be 5 picture-illustrated parts to each group of exercises. Let's take a basic push-up as an example to demonstrate how pictures and explanations are put together:

- First part will contain the demonstration of the basic push-up and how to do it.
- Second part will show the weighted movement. For example push-ups with a back pack loaded with plates, sand or other type of weight. Pay attention to this step as its specifics vary depending on the technique in question.
- Step three will demonstrate one or more variations of the unilateral assisted movement. For example you may do a one arm push-up while a partner uses a rope to pull you up.
- Step four will show how to descent into the pull of gravity. In most cases this step is very much self explanatory.
- Step five is the ultimate step before mastery. For example you can descent into the negative movement with one arm and get help from a partner or a resistance band when coming back up.

In case of similar exercises one will be demonstrated in full sequence, while others will only be seen as unilateral or bilateral variations. For example pull-ups and chin-ups are from the same family of techniques. Incline push-ups, flat push-ups and regular push-ups, dive bomber push-ups, are from the same family as well. Knowing the progression sequence for one will serve as an example for other similar techniques.

With that said, it is recommended to start with less difficult exercises. Master them, and while maintaining them, move on to more advanced ones. In many cases maintenance will come naturally through the process of mastering more challenging techniques. For example, unilateral rows should be worked on prior to one arm chin-ups. One hand push ups should be mastered prior to working on one arm shoulder presses. In many cases the process of shoulder press development will help to maintain the one arm push-ups.

This is not to say that once one arm push-up is mastered, it should be forgotten. The two exercises work partially different muscles groups and thus, should both be developed and maintained.

Rather than completely abandoning the one arm push-ups, you should do them after the one arm shoulder presses. If you want to practice both, yet don't have enough time or energy for the less challenging exercises, it is a good idea to do it in the second half of the day. You should be warned not to attempt to do the easier exercises in the alternative days with more challenging ones. This can lead to the over load on stabilizers, as well as common prime movers.

In other words, if Monday, Wednesday and Friday you work on shoulder presses, don't do regular one arm push-ups on Tuesday, Thursday and Saturday/Sunday. Instead focus on one pushing and one pulling movement. One arm row and one arm push-up is a perfect example of complimentary opposite movement. Do this on three non-consecutive days a week.

You don't have to wait for one of the techniques to be perfected, if you have mastered the other one. For example, you finally owned the one arm row, but still struggle with one arm push-up. Pat yourself on the back and keep working on unilateral push-up and move on to unilateral chin-up or dragon pull.

The lower body and mid-section don't always have a clear opposite exercise. It is also recommended to choose two or at most three exercises at one time and work on mastering their unilateral strength. Be careful to choose the exercises that don't use exactly the same muscle groups. For example, Beggar's Knees, One leg squat and Step-Up all utilize quadriceps heavily. An attempt to master all three at the same time can lead to over training and injury.

Another example of exercises utilizing similar muscle groups is Warrior III, Unilateral Dead Lift and Unilateral Cobra Bends. Having said that, the following schedule is just one of many potential ways to put together a training session. You can choose to work out 6 days a week, three non-consecutive days on the lower body and three on the upper. Usually two opposing exercises should be chosen for the upper body and two for the lower body. In case opposing exercises are not desired, the techniques should be chosen to have an absolute minimum utilization of the same muscle groups.

Here are some examples of non-opposite exercises that can be used together.

- Unilateral push-ups can be combined with unilateral pull-ups.
- Dragon pulls can be trained with over-head triceps presses.
- Hanging leg lift can be trained with shoulder flex or shoulder half-fly.
- On the lower body and mid-section side here are some possible non-opposing combinations:
    - One leg sit up can be combined with one leg toe presses.
    - Step up can be combined with warrior III.

As always please remember to use common sense and when in doubt post your question on ElasticSteel.net or Bodyweight culture.com forums where there are people who will gladly help you throughout your journey.

SECTION I
CHAPTER 2 - Push-ups
& Horizontal Rows

The first pair of complementary exercises is push-ups and horizontal rows. These are two basic exercises common to most Gravity Advantage Programs. The push-up direction of movement complements the horizontal rows. The two exercises use the same resistance and work exactly opposite muscle groups. Push-ups work the chest, shoulders, triceps with abdominals, hip flexors and quadriceps acting as main stabilizers. Rows, on the other hand, work the back of the shoulders, lattisimus dorsi, teres major, movers and stabilizers of the scapula. The isometric stabilization is provided by extensors or the spine, glutes and hamstrings. Those stabilizers are directly opposing the pushup stabilizers, the abdominals, hip flexors and quadriceps. These two exercises alone in their basic variation work most of your muscle groups, some dynamically others statically. In more advanced variations of those exercises different muscle groups can be recruited.

In case you have never worked on unilateral bodyweight movements, this is a good place to start. A mastery of one arm row and one arm push-up will add a great deal to most sports requiring unilateral skills. This chapter teaches a number of pushups and row variations. All of them can be mastered as a unilateral skill. It is best to start with the simplest variation first. Once mastered, you can move on to more advanced variations.

A word of warning, both horizontal pushing and horizontal pulling exercises greatly vary in difficulty. A Double Up pair is far more difficult than Yin Yang pair. Do not expect to be able to do a dive bomber push-up, up on the mastery of a basic one arm push-up. It is granted that most skills are connected, and flow into each other. It will be much easier for you to master a one arm bridge row after you have mastered a regular one arm row.

That said, it is recommended to retrace the steps for every new skill. For example, let's say you want to master a unilateral front up row upon mastering the basic row.

You would go back and try a bilateral front up row. If you can do 20 closed grip repetitions you can then move on to the next step. If you can't do 20 repetitions you would work on getting up to that number in one set. You would keep moving on to the next step till you find where you need work. All steps are outlined in the previous chapter.

In the following pages you will see the photographs demonstrating the steps needed to master these pairs:

- Yin Yang Pair = Basic One Arm Push-up + Basic One Arm Row
- Great Waves Pair = Hindu Push-ups + Hindu Rows
- Great Effort Pair = Back Up Push-ups + Front Up Rows
- Double Up Pair = Dive Bomber Push-ups + Sport Rows
- Beast Master Pair = Tiger Push-ups + Dragon Pulls
- Total Control Pair = Side Push-ups + Side Rows
- Total Containment Pair = Inside Pushups + Inside Rows

Beside those pairs of exercises many variations can be made out of basic Yin Yang pair. Plyometrics can be added to push-ups and/or rows. In terms of push-ups, the hand position can be changed. For example, fingers can point in different directions. Fist or finger tips can be used as well as push-up bars. For the rowing movement, variations can be added as well. You can adopt the over hand or under hand grip. You can use a rope, "USA (Universal Strength Apparatus)", or a stick placed on two chairs.

Both "Yin and Yang" can change the angle and adjust just how parallel they are to the floor. You can place your hands or feet on a chair while doing the push-ups. You can elevate the hand or feet while working on the row. To see many great bilateral examples of how to add lots of fun to the basic movement, take a look at " The Push-up and pull-up book". It contains dozens upon dozens of examples of bodyweight exercise variations.

As far as the push-up, is concerned, there is no equipment needed for this exercise. Rows on the other hand require a bar to be placed parallel to the floor at a height slightly higher than extended arm length from the back of the shoulder to the palm of the hand. (Tip: If you are looking just for the upper body workout with no gym equipment, take a look at the original Gravity Advantage text.)

If you have the Universal Strength Apparatus™ everything becomes much easier because the level of difficulty can be adjusted with simply getting a hold of higher or lower rungs on the apparatus.

Assuming that you are using a bar and two chairs for the row and the floor for push-ups, you will need some kind of a weighted or resistive devise to use as resistance as well as the supporting devise to be used as assistance. Please re-read the five steps if you are unclear for the need of the resistive or assistive device. Once again you can use the resistance in the form of a heavy book bag, weighted vest, resistance band, partner pressure. Assistance to one arm exercises can be added through the use of the partner's help or resistance bands.

Two Contra Lateral Core (CLC) exercises are recommended for the pushups-rows pairs. These exercises develop the midsection in such a way that its muscles can handle the load of oblique line of pull. For example, when a basic one arm push-up is executed with your right arm, the line of pull is from the right arm through the upper right quadrant of the trunk, to the lower left quadrant of the trunk, and to the left leg.

Even the muscles of the left leg must work harder than they would if the push-up was performed with both arms. In that light it's essential to prepare the body for right stabilization work. Three progressive pairs of bodyweight CLC exercises are recommended. They are demonstrated starting from the easiest to the most challenging. It is recommended to master a 15-20 seconds hold of level two or three CLC exercises prior to attempting the unilateral assisted training, which is the third step of Power of One progressions.

Hundreds of free bodyweight exercises, routines, workouts, contests and so much more. If you haven't already signed up, visit bodyweightculture.com!

One Arm Push-ups Progression

Step 1

The first step requires you to master at least 20 close grip push-ups.

- Start each rep with hands together and arms locked out
- Lower you chest so that it's almost touching the floor
- Then press back up.

Step 2

The second step requires you to lift at least half of your push-up , even though two thirds is more preferable. To find out your pushup weight, place your hands on the scale in the pushup position. In this case a heavy bag is used for variety. You can use anything from partner resistance, a back pack, a weighted vest to resistance bands. Aim for 2-5 repetitions before moving on to the next step.

One Arm Push-ups Progression

Step 3

Assisted One Arm push-up is the third step. In this case elastic assistance is utilized. The goal is to have enough resistance to do 2-3 repetitions. Decrease the assistance when at least two consecutive workouts yield more than 2-3 repetitions. Sets depend on training load and the amount of techniques and skills trained at the same time. 2-5 sets are recommended. Do not do this more than 3 non-consecutive times a week.

Step 4

Negatives is the fourth stage. Your first try will determine whether or not you are ready for eccentric training. If you fall uncontrollably onto the floor, that would imply that you are not ready. On the other hand, if you were able to descend with even some amount of control, you can stay with this step.

One Arm Push-ups Progression

Step 5

This is the last step in mastery of one arm push-up. You are ready for this stage when you can do a full range of motion negative, while pausing at any specific point in movement for at least a few seconds. Step five calls for unassisted negatives and lightly assisted positive. There are many ways to provide the concentric assistance. Here, the simplest method is shown. You simply descend with one arm and then use the other arm to help yourself back up. The utilization of the helping arm should be kept to a minimum.

Be sure to be on a lookout for our Encyclopedia of Puh-ups and Pull-ups.

This book takes a look at many innovative variations of both exercises. Many rarely seen variations are demonstrated. It also discusses proven and tested methods of developing strength, power in total movement as well as separate muscle groups. Several programs on top of developing high repetition sets are discussed. This is a must have for a serious fitness enthusiast.

One Arm Row Progression

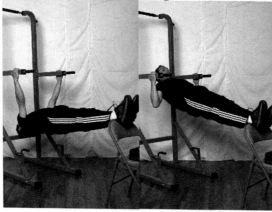

<u>Step 1</u>

This is the first stage in one arm row progression. The aim is 20 well controlled rows. In this case a bodyweight station and chairs are used as equipment. You can use any object, which height is your arm length. Your feet can be on the floor or raised. Medium grip is demonstrated, but you should practice the narrow and wide grip as well for variety.

<u>Step 2</u>

This is the second step in Power of One progression for rows. Weighted rows are demonstrated. For variety purpose the feet are raised and held in place by the Universal Strength Apparatus. The resistance is provided by the sand filled book bag. Weighted vest, resistance band, partner resistance are among other methods of adding resistance to the rows.

One Arm Row Progression

Step 3

This is the third step in the two arm to one arm row progression. Two ways of using resistance band for assistance are demonstrated. The top picture, which shows the starting position shows the use of resistance band, when it's held with non pulling arm. On the bottom picture the resistance band is made into a loop and is placed around the arm.

Step 4

This is the fourth stage of one arm rows progressions.

- You are to use both hands to pull yourself up to the flex arm position.
- When the arms are flexed let go of one arm and use the other to descend. **Make sure that your grip is strong enough to prevent you from falling.**

- ***Please note that:*** The set up shown on the photo is demonstrated for variety and is performed by a professional. When first starting out you may want to use a bar just an arm's length above the floor. You may want to keep your feet off the floor. Keeping a break fall prop such as a pillow may be helpful when first training this technique.

One Arm Row Progression

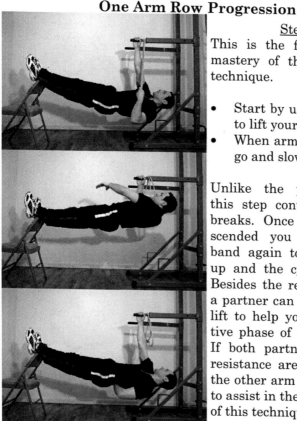

Step 5

This is the final stage for mastery of this one armed technique.

- Start by using assistance to lift yourself up.
- When arms are flexed let go and slowly descend.

Unlike the previous step, this step continues without breaks. Once you have descended you will use the band again to pull yourself up and the cycle continues. Besides the resistance band, a partner can provide a light lift to help you with a positive phase of the movement. If both partner and elastic resistance are not available, the other arm can be utilized to assist in the positive phase of this technique.

THE GRAVITY ADVANTAGE
MAX
A guide that teaches you how to utilize your total body weight to develop TREMENDOUS STRENGTH and GREAT LOOKING PHYSIQUE

Paul Zaichik

If you're tired of endless push-ups and want to not only spice up your training routine, but bring your strength to a new level then **Gravity Advantage MAX** is for you! **Gravity Advantage Max** is a complete bodyweight training program that takes your strength and Power to the Max in every sense of the word. 12 Powerful sequences are illustrated with one thing in mind - Full advantage of your bodyweight for maximum strength.

Push ups are great, but you can do dozens of them. GAM teaches moves that are all strength, low reps high resistance. The program covers every muscle in the body to develop a rock solid, machine-like physique. The program is absolutely balanced, developing equal but great force in every muscle and its antagonist. Everyone who masters all 12 GAM techniques will have the strength of a top quality athlete. The great advantage of this program is that only bodyweight resistance is used. You just have to know what moves to do and how to progress. It's well designed, scientifically progressive program of bodyweight strength training. No pages are wasted here. This is a full body, maximum gains program for any conditioning level. **Gravity Advantage MAX - *Get Your Copy Today!***

Great Waves Pair *Bilateral* Variation

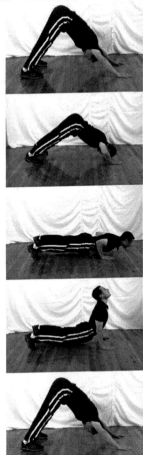

Hindu Push-ups and Hindu Rows is a variation of basic Push-ups and rows. Hindu push-ups start from the flexed hip position. Then the hips are raised to the suspended bridge position. Following that, the hips are lifted toward the bar and lowered in a wave like motion into the starting position.

Hindu push-ups start in a downward facing dog position, then the body is lowered and raised in a waive motion. Once in the upward facing dog the arms remain straight and the hips are raised into the starting position.

Great Waves Pair *Uni*lateral Variation

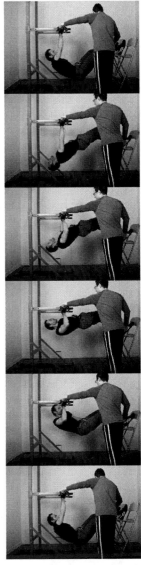

On this page one arm variations of the great waves pair is demonstrated.

Notice the progression sequence is the same as for other push-ups and row variations. Notice that in the depiction of rows a partner holds the bar and the chair in order to secure the safety of the athlete. The major difference between the regular and Hindu row set up, is the clearance height from the floor. Both hands and feet must be elevated to allow the hips and the head to drop low when needed. One arm Hindu Push-ups are performed exactly the same way as the two arm variation. The other hand is usually kept behind the back.

Double Up Pair *Bi*lateral Variation

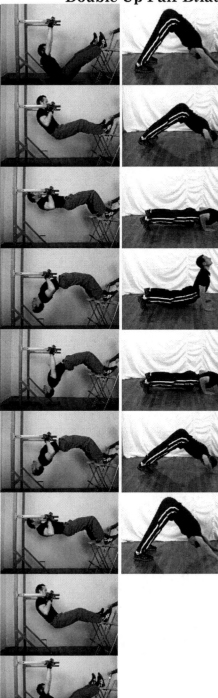

Dive Bomber

The double up pair consists of a Dive Bomber push-ups and sport rows. Both techniques are actually two techniques in one. The Sport Row calls for a pull to the bar followed by a descent into a suspended bridge as the first half of the exercise. The second half reverses the movement by rowing the body up in a bridged position prior to coming back down into the starting position.

The Dive Bomber Push-ups starts in a downward facing dog position. An assumption is made that there is a bar right above the hands. The head goes under that bar and comes up on the other side. Then the reverse movement brings the body under the bar and back into its starting position.

Double Up Pair _Uni_lateral Variation

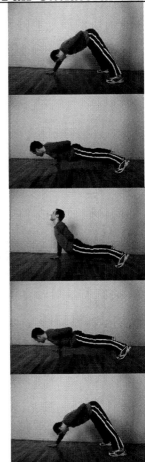

The One Armed Double Up pair is performed exactly like the two arm variation. Use the Power of One five step progression to build up to these two great techniques.

Great Effort Pair *Bi*lateral Variation

The Great Effort pair has a large focus on overhead concentric training. The Front Up rows begin by performing the first part of the Sport Row. Once in the suspended bridge position the hips are simply dropped into the starting position, while the arms remain straight.

The Back Up push-ups is essentially the second part of the Dive Bomber Push-up. Starting from the downward facing dog position, the hips are dropped into the upward facing dog position. Following that the body moves under the imaginary bar leading with the hips until it ends up in the starting position.

Great Effort Pair *Uni*lateral Variation

Use the five steps of Power of One progression to master the unilateral variation. Just like the previous technique the high bar and foot placement is essential for the rowing movement, due to required clearance for the hips and the head. Make sure that your grip is up for the challenge, and the equipment set up is stable. Possibly have a spotter help you, when you are working on this technique.

Beast Master Pair *Bilateral* Variation

Tiger Push-ups (*Bi*lateral)

The beast master pair can be seen as the intermediate between the push-ups and hand stand push-ups, the rows and the pull ups.

The pushing part of the beast master pair is called the tiger push-ups.

To do this exercise, place the soles of your feet on the wall, place your hands next to each other with your hips raised. Lower your head toward your hands and press back up.

The Dragon Pull (*Bi*lateral)

The pulling exercise is called the Dragon Pull.

This exercise requires a bar which is attached to a wall or to a bodyweight station as seen in the picture above.

Hang on the bar first and place your feet on the wall or vertical bar at approximately your hip level. Once in position pull your chest toward the bar. Return to the straight arm position. A basic over hand grip is demonstrated above, but any variety of grips can be employed. Master 20 repetitions of this exercise and gradually progress through the 5 steps of Power of One program to master the unilateral variations illustrated on the next page.

Beast Master Pair *Uni*lateral Variation

<u>Tiger Push-ups (*Uni*lateral)</u>

The one arm variation of the Tiger Push-ups is very similar to the two arm variation, except that one arm is used.

Use a soft mat or a pillow as crash pad for your head especially when just starting to work on the negatives.

<u>Attention! Be very careful with this exercise.</u> If you feel you're not ready for it, do not attempt it, as it may be dangerous.

<u>The Dragon Pull(*Uni*lateral)</u>

This is the unilateral variation of the dragon pull. When first working on this technique make sure that your grip is well conditioned and you can safely jump off and land on your feet if the grip fails.

CLC Training For the *Uni*lateral Push-ups

These are the CLC (Contra Lateral Core) sequence which is recommended to be mastered toward the end of the second step of Power of One program.

The main goal of this program is to develop core strength to support the unilateral movement. As you can see,

the grip strength is a positive side effect of CLC training.

There are three steps starting from the basic to the most advanced.

- One arm support with both knees bent is the first step. Upon mastery of this step, you can move on to the intermediate step.

- The second step calls for straight legged one arm hold. You will find that holding the legs straight is more difficult than having them bent. Once you are comfortable with this step, one leg should be lifted up. The leg that's lifted should be on the same side as the supported leg. For example, in the photo above, the right arm is holding and the right leg is lifted.

- Master at least 15-20 seconds of the advanced hold and you are ready to start the third step of Power of One program which is the assisted unilateral training. CLC sequence for push-ups mimics the one used for rows. The basic hold is rested on three points; one arm and two knees. If your knees are not used to the hard floor, knee pads or a mat is advised. Perfect this and the next step is waiting for you.

- Here straight arm unilateral push-up position is held. Once comfortable with this exercise you can lift the leg on the same side of the supporting arm and practice the advanced variation.

Total Control Pair Side Push-ups

Step 1

The side push-up is a pushing component of the Total Control Pair. While the side push-up is executed with the bottom arm, both arms are used in the first stage of Power of One program.

Yoga blocks or a short stool can be used to provide elevation for the top arm. The top arm should be elevated just enough to keep it as straight as possible at the top of the movement. The goal here is to keep the top shoulder over the bottom shoulder as much as possible. The feet can be on top of each other or the top foot can be in front of the bottom one. Work this technique until at least 20 good repetitions are mastered.

Step 2

The weighted variation is exactly the same as the non-weighted one. Book bag filled with sand is used in the picture above.

You can use other resistance apparatus such as elastic resistance, weighted vest or partner pressure.

Total Control Pair Side Push-ups

Step 3

This is the third stage of Power of One progression for the side push-up. While the bottom arm performs the exercise the top arm assists only slightly. Once again a resistance band attached over head or a manual assistance from a partner can be substituted as assistance mechanism.

Step 4

The fourth step of this Power of One program is the unassisted negatives. It is most likely that you will experience pretty good control at the top few inches of this technique. As you approach the floor the exercise will get more difficult. This has to do with the position of the shoulder joint and the unfamiliarity of the range of motion. If you find that the top half or one third of the movement is rather easy, but the bottom is not at all possible, weighted negatives can be applied. To do this you will add resistance and continue to do the upper portion of the movement. When the resistance is removed the extra strength, even from a different range of motion, will carry you deeper into the side push-up with more control.

Total Control Pair Side Push-ups

Step 5

This is the fifth stage. Don't get confused; this is not a return to the square one. Instead the top arm provides no help when the body is lowered. It only provides minimal assistance on the upward part of the technique. If the question comes up as to exactly how much help does upper arm gives, you can try to use only the finger tips of the top arm. You can also use the resistance band or a partner to raise your body. If the resistance band it used, it should be held with the top hand and only relied upon when the concentric movement is called for.

The Gravity Advantage

Upper Body Conditioning Book. Learn how to develop a truly functional strength in your core muscles without endless abdominal exercises. No equipment necessary.

The Gravity Advantage MAX Book

Everyone who honestly follows this program for a few months, has a potential to not only be able to develop a ripped muscular physique, but also muscular might, never before thought possible, without ever lifting weights. The secret of this program is the progressive loading of muscle groups through the use of one's own body weight and gravity.

Total Control Pair Side Rows

Step 1

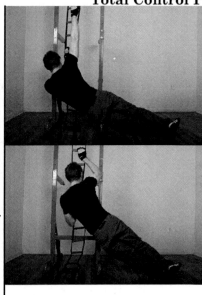

This is the first step in uni-lateral side row training. Initially both arms are used. Start this exercise by hanging sideways with your top arm outstretched. The bottom arm should be pulled across the body enabling it to horizontally extend and abduct at the shoulder in order to pull the body up. Using both arms pull yourself up and than lower yourself down. Aim at 20 consecutive repetitions with good form and straight torso.

Step 2

This is the second step to side row achievement. A weighted two arm side and inside row is performed. The technique is exactly the same as demonstrated in the first step, but this time a book bag is used to increase the resistance.

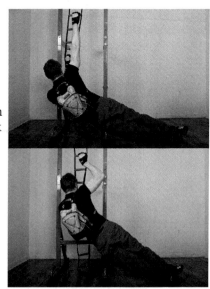

Total Control Pair Side Rows

Step 3

Third step of Power of One program calls for unilateral assisted rows. In the pictures you can see the left arm performing the rows and the right arm assisting it. If you have the luxury of a partner or a resistance band to aid in your movement feel free to use that as well.

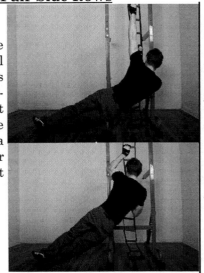

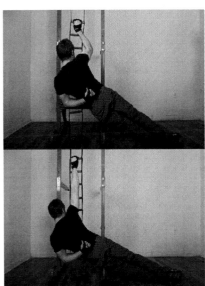

Step 4

Once you feel pretty comfortable with assisted movement, negatives are next. Use both arms to lift yourself up and then use only the top arm to lower yourself into the pull of gravity. If you realize that you can't control the descent and fall uncontrollably, the implication is; you have entered the fourth step prematurely. More work is needed in the third step. It's important to note that besides the biceps, lats, and posterior deltoid this exercise also develops the forearm and midsection as stabilization muscles.

Total Control Pair Side Rows

Step 5

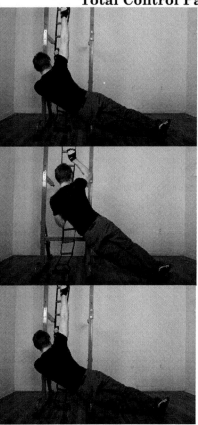

This is the firth step. Both arms remain in contact with the USA at all times.

Unlike the step four where a break is taken after every attempt. Step five is continuous.

Use the top arm with only slight assistance of the bottom arm to ascend. Then using only your top arm come back down. Notice, that the supporting left hand provides no assistance on the descent.

Total Containment Pair Inside Push-ups

Step 1

This is the first step in the inside push-up progression sequence. The same exercise is used as the side push-up to get started. From now on, the focus will be on strengthening the top arm, which pushes down and across the body. Most people will find this exercise rather difficult, yet very rewarding when it's finally mastered.

Once again the set up calls for prop elevation to place the top arm on. The bottom arm rests on the floor. Both arms flex on the descent and extend on the ascent. The goal is to keep the trunk straight and the shoulders in vertical line, one over the other. The twisting of the trunk should be kept to a minimum.

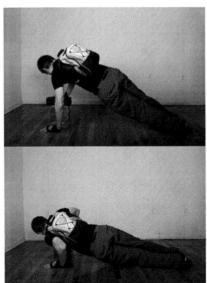

Step 2

Second step is exactly the same technique as the first step. The difference is extra resistance. You can use anything that will provide the resistance for you. Weighed book bag, weighted vest or a resistance band have the advantage due to measurable weight increments. An experienced partner can provide gradual incremental resistance as well.

Total Containment Pair Inside Push-ups

Step 3

The third step of Power of One program for inside push-up looks exactly the same as the one for the side push-up.

Looks can be deceiving. In reality it's the opposite that is happening. This time it's the top arm that does most of the work, with the bottom arm only providing slight assistance.

Step 4

This is the fourth step, involving unassisted negatives. You will know if you are ready for this step the second you try it. If you experience a complete lack of control this means that step three is calling you back.

Don't be discouraged. Simply return to the third step and try your best to maximize the utilization of the top arm and minimize the assistance of the bottom arm.

Total Containment Pair Inside Push-ups
Step 5

This is the firth step. Although it looks like the first and third step it's not. Here, multiple repetitions of inside push-ups are performed in each set.

The negative movement has been mastered and the positive is only slightly assisted. The bottom arm remains on the floor throughout the exercise, but does no work during the eccentric part of the exercise.

It helps to push up only a tiny bit and then let go when it's time to come back down.

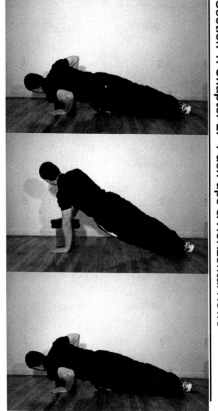

Core Transformation

Stay tuned for this incredible book! This book is about functional core development. In most athletic or everyday movement the core serves as a stabilizer or a center for power transfer. This book discusses many ways of training the core for specific sport or everyday related functions. Many exercises don't even appear to have anything to do with mid-section, that is, until you try them. This book will open your eyes about the true nature of functional core training. Visit bodyweightculture.com, elastic-steel.net or paulzaichik.com for more information.

Total Containment Pair Inside Rows

Step 1

Here is the antagonist of the inside push-up; the inside row. The first step to master it is the two armed combination of the inside and side row.

In case you have already mastered the side row, you will have a tendency to pull more with the top arm. There may also be a tendency to initiate the pull with the top arm and then follow with the bottom arm. Try to find a comfortable range of motion for the inside arm and stay with that range.

Step 2

This is the weighted variation. Once again stay away from top arm domination tendency and focus on the bottom arm.

Find a range of motion where your inside rowing arm is comfortable in exerting force. Stay in that range and gradually increase it.

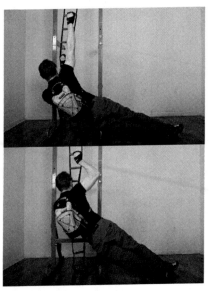

Total Containment Pair Inside Rows

Step 3

Third stage is unilateral assisted inside rows. Using the USA is the simplest way to work on this step. Simply have the top arm minimize it's work.

If you are working with a partner, have him gently raise and lower your torso, while you use the bottom arms.

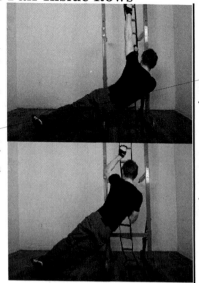

Step 4

Now comes time to tease gravity. Use both arms to get yourself into the top position and keep holding on with only your bottom hand, while your top hand is behind your back (pic 1.).

This step requires a lot of concentration. Descent down to mimic the second picture. Take a short break and try again, possibly with the other arm.

Total Containment Pair Inside Rows

Step 5

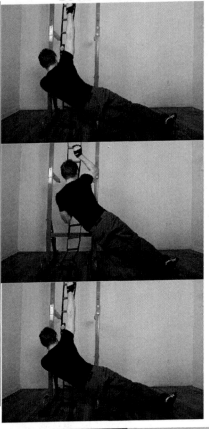

Here comes the last step. Negative movement is mastered and now only the positive remains. We can't do it yet, so a little bit of help will do. Use the top arm to guide yourself up and only the bottom one to get down. Soon you will develop an ability to use only the bottom arm and the glory will be yours.

Bodyweight Training in Depth

Be sure to visit www.ElasticSteel.net for more information about this one of a kind ONLINE TRAINING COURSE brought to you by Paul Zaichik.

This course covers every part of your body and shows you how bodyweight training can target any specific muscle group or a needed movement. The world of bodyweight training is taken out of contest of few popular exercises such as dips and crunches and explored through it's full spectrum. A person walking away form this course will know how to train for any specific goal using only his or her own weight.

SECTION I
CHAPTER 3
Heaven & Earth

This chapter teaches a pair of exercises called Heaven and Earth. The goal of this progression is to master one arm over head pushing and pulling force. The pulling takes the place of a chin-up, a pull-up and their variations. The pushing technique, takes place instead of bodyweight shoulder press. Notice this is not a handstand push-up. Since gravity advantage likes to focus on more or less equal opposite force, the shoulder press is a better opposing pair to the one arm chin-up or pull-up then unilateral handstand push-up.

It is recommended that you master the one arm push-up and one arm row as described in previous chapter, prior to working on the Heaven and Earth pair. You can practice the two handed pull-ups and shoulder presses after your push-ups/row workouts within the same session. If you need help mastering these movements as well as other full body pushing/ pulling movements please see the "Gravity Advantage Max Book" for maximum resistance bodyweight exercises.

Upon having mastered the exercises in the previous chapter you can work on the Heaven and Earth pair as the first part of your work out. For cool down, a few sets of unilateral push-ups/rows can be performed at the end of the workout. This will be a nice way to maintain the one arm horizontal rows and push-ups.

Any single skill should not hold back any other skill. For example, suppose you mastered the one arm horizontal row, yet are struggling with one arm push-up. Does this mean that you have to stay with a Yin Yang pair until the one arm push-up is mastered? This of course is your choice. The good news is that you do have a choice. You can move on with the pulling skill, while still working on the pushing skill. For example, you can arrange you training session in the following way. While continuing to train the one arm push-up according to Power of One sequence you can begin to work on your mastery of 20 chin-ups. Suppose you were able to master the 20 chin-ups and yet can't do one good single arm push-up.

You would then arrange your workout like this:

- The first part of your workout will be the highest step (i.e. step 5) of power of one program. You can either make the chin-up training as the second part of your program or intertwine the two.
- Let's assume you are working on a unilateral assisted push-ups, which is a step three. At the same time you are working on weighted closed grip chin-ups, which is step two. So you would do a left hand assisted push-up set, then a right hand assisted push-up set. (If you are left handed you would do the right arm first.)
- After a short break you would do a weighted chin-up set. Then you would repeat the push-ups, followed by chin-ups.
- At the end of the work out you can do a few sets of one arm horizontal rows just for maintenance.

If you are looking for variations of heaven and earth pair, plenty are available; a chin-up can be substituted for a pull-up, the hanging rope can be used as well. The shoulder press can be performed on a push-up bar, fist, finger tips, etc. For dozens and dozens of creative bilateral variations please refer to the Push-up & Pull up book.

Heaven and Earth pair requires some very basic equipment. Pull-ups require a stable overhead bar, Universal Strength Apparatus or any other suspended equipment can be used as well. The shoulder press requires something to elevate your feet, a chair or table is one option. In some cases a wall can used to place the feet on. Keep in mind that the lower your feet are, the more posterior chain flexibility is required. If you are interested in stretching and flexibility please take a look at ElasticSteel flexibility products.

The five steps outlined in the first chapter should be followed to master this pair, just like any other pair. While working on the first two steps, core exercises should be trained. Those will enable the stabilizers of the midsection to do their work as one arm techniques are developed. There is a progression sequence of three mid-section exercise pairs for this part of the program. One progression is aimed at pulling one arm techniques, the other for pushing. At least a second level should be mastered prior to moving on to the assisted one arm chin-ups or shoulder presses. 15-20 seconds struggle free mastery should be achieved as the mark of mastery.

Heaven and Earth Progression Chin-Ups

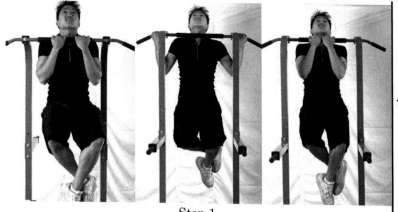

<u>Step 1</u>

The pulling part of the Heaven and Earth pair can be any type of free handing vertical pulling movement. There are dozens and dozens of variations available. If you would like to see them please see our Push-up/Pull-up book.

For our purposes we will demonstrate the Power of One progression using chin-ups. Chin-ups are performed with palms facing toward you, with an underhand or supinated grip. It is recommended to develop 20 chin-ups using all three grip widths in training.

The three grips are illustrated above. The regular, wide and narrow grip. Take care to descend into a straight arm, dead hang and come up to a full flexed arm position, with your chin reaching over the bar. Once in a while you can throw in other grip styles, such a pull-ups or over hand grip for variety.

Heaven and Earth Progression Chin-Ups

Step 2

This is the second step in mastering a one arm chin-up. To escape boredom and demonstrate possible training variety, a heavy medicine ball is used as resistance. Back pack, heavy bag, resistance bands, partner pressure, and weighted vest are just some of the options.

Aim to progressively increase the resistance until you can lift at least 1/2 of your body weight on top of the normal resistance lifted every time you do a chin-up. If you can lift 2/3 of your body weight even better. In other words, if you weigh 200lbs you should lift at least 100lbs of extra weight.

Step 3

Progressing to the third stage unilateral assistance comes into play. In this case a resistance band is used. For a left handed chin-up, the right hand is used for assistance.

The trick is to extend the resistance band while pulling yourself up. The lower your arm is on the band, the less assistance will be provided. In case you have access to the gym and an assisted dip/chin-up station is available, you can use it as well.

Heaven and Earth Progression Chin-Ups

Step 4

Here go the negative. Many people who train for one arm chin-ups start their training with the eccentric movement.

In our book the word "NEGATIVE" is truly negative if you are not ready for it. The risk of injury raises when second and third step of training is skipped. You have been warned.

There are a number of ways to practice this technique. The first is to chin-up with both hands and then let go of one hand and fight gravity unilaterally. The other is to use only one arm and jump up to the flexed arm position using your legs and the momentum. Once up there, begin the descent holding on with one hand.

Step 5

The last step is an assisted positive and a non-assisted negative. Use the resistance band to assist yourself up. Then leg go off the band and fight gravity on the way down. If you can, pause a few times. In the picture above the first pause is when the chin dips below the bar and second is when the arm is about 90 degrees bent at the elbow. Once you are in a dead hang, grip the resistance band and repeat the whole thing.

Heaven and Earth Pulling *Uni*lateral and *Bi*lateral Over hand and Neutral Pull-Ups

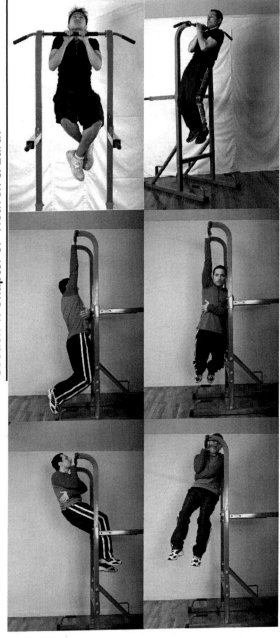

Here is the demonstration of the other two common pulling variations of heaven and earth. On the left is the pull-up and one arm pull-up. On the right is the neutral grip pull-up and its one armed variation.

Use the same exact progression sequence as used for one arm chin-up to master these two power moves.

Do not be discouraged if the mastery of one arm chin-up won't automatically give you the mastery of these two techniques. Just retrace the Power of One steps and you will prevail.

Heaven and Earth Progression Shoulder Press

Step 1

Here comes the pushing part of Heaven and Earth. This is an incredible shoulder strengthener. Take a look at two armed variation. The body goes into the inverted L. Arms and torso vertical and legs parallel to the floor. This exercise is also a connecting exercise in Gravity Advantage Max Book, leading up to the handstand push-ups. The exercise is rather simple once you are in position.

From straight arms, lower your head down and press back up. If you are up for it, this exercise can also be performed with feet on the wall. If something goes wrong have a mat ready and be prepared to roll out of this position. If you don't know how to roll, an experienced spotter will be a good idea (Do not try to perform this exercise if you do not know how to roll correctly or you will get injured).

If it so happens that this exercise is out of your present reach, go back to push-ups and master the back up push-ups, the feet on chair push-ups, and the tiger push-ups. Those will strengthen your shoulders and prepare you for the over head

Heaven and Earth Progression Shoulder Press

Step 2

Once 20 good reps are mastered in the first step, feel free to proceed to the second step. In the photo above the resistance bands are used for increased resistance.

There are other options of course; Your partner can place a heavy bag on your lower pelvis. If you have a weighted vest or a book back that won't slide down it can be a valuable resistive tool as well.

Be very careful while performing this exercise resisted. Always have a pre-planned escape, if it goes awry. Everything must be stable. The chairs used in the pictures are actually held in place. If the feet are too move, they would be grabbed and held by a spotter.

Aim to add at least 40% of your bodyweight to this exercise prior to moving on. If you have an access to the gym, feel free to utilize the equipment there. Resistance bands, cables, dumbbells or barbells can be used to increase the power in overhead pressing.

ATTENTION!

Those exercises should be used as supplements rather than a total workout. If you choose to use them, carefully mix them in with body weight training.

Be careful not to over train. A shoulder injury is often slow to heal and quick to regain. Move slower and cautiously and you will get further with this technique.

Heaven and Earth Progression Shoulder Press

Step 3

The photos demonstrating the third step may look exactly like the first step, but they are not. One arm does more work than the other. If you have really worked on step two, you should be able to shift more than half the effort to one arm. In case it's too difficult to calculate exactly how much work each side is doing, other options exist. A resistance band can be hanged and placed under the hips. It's best placed under your hip flexors by a partner.

Another option is to have your partner help you lower and raise your body by holding you by the hips. If this option is chosen make sure that your partner is strong enough to do the assisting.

Training for Combat in Depth

This course is designed for combat trainers and their athletes. Dozens and dozens of strength training exercises are taught for specific combat applications. Techniques such as punches and throws are analyzed and broken down into trainable units. The goal is to learn exercises and drills to punch harder, move faster, and have more intensity behind each technique.

This ONLINE COURSE is taught by Paul Zaichik. This is a 12 weeks course which consists of follow along classes, presented to the trainee every week. Here you will have the opportunity to showcase your progress to Paul Zaichik and get his feedback on your progress.

Heaven and Earth Progression Shoulder Press

Step 4
By now you have probably spent a good amount of time and effort on the previous step, now comes the first chance to test if all your efforts pay off.

If you haven't used a thick mat or a pillow yet, now may be a good time. Unlike a one arm pull-up where letting go and landing on feet ends all worries, the only way to compensate for lack of strength is to roll out of position.

Unfortunately, the second part of the movement is much harder than the first. This implies that you may not decide to roll until it's too late. **Use caution**.

ATTENTION!

Here are the suggestions:

1. Do not try this until there is a solid mastery of the first three steps.
2. Unlike the pictures, keep the other arm ready to break your fall. Don't place it behind your back.
3. Have a shock absorbent material waiting under your head. Wearing a protective helmet is not a bad idea either. Combining the two of them is even better.

Heaven and Earth Progression Shoulder Press

<u>Step 5</u>

This is the fifth stage. If you're here this means that you have mastered the controlled negatives and are ready to go all the way. After using one arm to descend, use the other arm to help yourself back up. If a partner is available, have him give you a slight boost on the upward part of the movement.

Pat yourself on the back upon mastering this move. You have won some major bragging rights!

SECTION I
CHAPTER 4
Two Shoulder Joint Strengthening Pairs:
Total Reach 1 & Total Reach 2

This chapter shows you the key to mastery of two shoulder joint strengthening pairs. They are named Total Reach I and Total Reach Two respectively. Although these exercises strengthen the muscles that move and stabilize the shoulder joint, they also transform the abdominals into a mighty wall to be reckoned with.

In most unilaterally dominant sports, the shoulder is a place where power is transferred from the trunk to the arm. The Total Reach pairs are primed training techniques for getting the advantage of this transfer. Not only do they super strengthen the shoulder, they also prepare the midsection to support the effort. Activities that can benefit from these are tennis, swimming, boxing, wrestling, baseball, football, handball and many others.

Prior to beginning the exercises in this chapter it would help if the Yin Yang pair is mastered. Heaven and Earth mastery is recommended, but is not absolutely necessary.

Total reach I pair consists of two exercises. A Superman pull I or a unilateral roll out and a shoulder flex. The first exercise can be performed either using the Universal Strength Apparatus or a rolling piece of equipment such as an abs dolly, or a rolling dumbbell.

The second exercise can be performed using the Universal Strength Apparatus (USA) or another type of suspended equipment. The Superman pull (If USA is used) or unilateral roll out (If a rolling equipment is used) works the lattisimus dorsi, teres major (upper back muscles), lower chest, and triceps. While forearm muscles, as well as the core and front of the legs stabilize the movement.

The second technique, rightfully named "shoulder flex" strengthens the muscles of the shoulder, while the wrist, forearm, core and posterior chain provides the static support.

The progression of the first exercise in pair depends on which equipment is used. You can use the Power of One progression or the program described below. Notice, this program utilizing the rolling equipment is only described, not demonstrated.

Keep in mind that this is slightly different progression than the Power of One five steps. If the rolling equipment is used the following is a recommended routine to progress from two armed to one armed movement.

At first the two armed technique must be mastered and this is a challenge in of itself. The basic protocol is to start at the on your knees and master this part. Later on you can use weighted resistance while still practicing the roll outs on your knees. Following this, the weighted vest or a back pack should be removed and straight leg variation should be trained. If you can't go all the way out or come up after having rolled too far out, try the following; stand in front of the wall and roll out to the wall and back. With time you should be able to move further and further from the wall, until the wall is no longer needed. At this point the same protocol can be repeated for one arm. At first, the one arm roll outs on the knees should be trained. Following that the weight should be used. Next, straight legs, one armed roll out to the wall should be worked on until the point that the wall is no longer needed.

If you have the USA in your possession, the mastery of the superman pull I becomes a bit easier. You can use the five step program with the USA, as well or instead of, assisted one arm exercise; you can simply use the higher handle, making the exercise easier. While utilizing the negatives make sure to keep the free arm holding on the other part of the USA to prevent the fall at full extension. When working on the last step, you can use the non-working arm to help press back up as assisted positive.

The bilateral shoulder flex is a challenging technique. Take care to perfect this technique. Progress from the upper handles to the lower ones using both hands first.

Once lower handles are mastered, it's time to apply the Power of One Five step program. The first two steps are self explanatory. The third step calls for assisted one arm training. Using upper handles with less resistance does the trick. Once negatives are trained on step four, second arm can be of help to get into the starting position. In other words, use both arms to flex the shoulders and get the arms up. Then let go with one arm and defy gravity with the other. You can also start this with a higher handle and go lower as you get stronger. The advantages of having multi-level handles of Universal Strength Apparatus are or great help here.

Lastly for the final Power of One level, you can use the assisting arm to get up to the position and primary arm to fight gravity. Unlike the previous level, here negative and positive movements flow into each other and no breaks are taken every time a negative is performed.

Total Reach II is the second pair in this chapter. It consists of a side roll out or a Superman II and a Side Wave. The two exercises are supplementary to the Total Reach I pair. While they can be trained on their own, it is best to master the Total Reach I first.

The Superman II or a Side Roll Out work approximately the same muscle groups as its close relative. The slight difference is in the fibers of the upper back and lower chest. The stabilization is provided by core muscles flexing the spine to the side rather than forward with slight rotation. Also the lower body adductors and abductors get engaged for the front of the legs.

The shoulder press uses approximately the same core and lower body stabilizers as its opposing exercises. The true opposition is in the upper body, where the middle deltoid takes the bulk of labor, assisted by anterior deltoid and muscles of the shoulder girdle.

If the Superman Pull I is mastered it's only a matter of time before its sideways cousin is also perfected. All of the five steps of Power of One programs can be retraced, or you can simply start with higher (lower difficulty) handles and work on increasing the difficulty as new level of strength develops.

Shoulder Over development is slightly different than regular Power of One program. No two sided variation exists, so the Side Wave is combined with Superman II as level one technique. Weighted variation is applied to master the second level. One arm movement with fingers of the other arm assisting, is the third step of Power of One program for this exercise. Eccentric unilateral struggle with gravity comprise the fourth stage. Finally unassisted negatives and light positive movement assistance takes the Shoulder Over to the fight level of unilateral mastery.

The core should also be trained, especially in preparation for Total Reach I pair. Same exercises that are used for Push-up and Horizontal Rows should be used here. In case the Yin Yang pair has been mastered, it is possible to skip the core training.

Latest Online Courses Offered by Paul Zaichik

Kicking Technique in Depth

This course teaches absolutely everything one needs to know to develop super sharp kicking techniques. Tests are demonstrated to find out the weak link of your techniques and fix it. Special exercises are taught to improve every area of the kicks. Main focus is on speed, power, endurance, precision, focus, height, control, and timing.

Splits and Flexibility in Depth

This course dives deep into the ElasticSteel principles and how they are applied to general flexibility and splits. Muscle groups and their respective stretches are taught in correct sequences. Many modalities that assist in muscle relaxation and facilitate stretching techniques are explained.

These are 12 weeks courses which consist of follow along classes, presented to the trainee every week. Here you will have the opportunity to showcase your progress to Paul Zaichik and get his feedback on your progress.

Total Reach I Superman Pull

Step 1

Superman pull is the Total Reach I first exercise. This exercise is performed with a suspension equipment. Start by leaning slightly forward and keep your arms parallel to the floor.

Slowly and with control bring your arms up. Ideally there should be a straight line from your hands to your feet. The mid-section should not sag or arch. Using the strength of your chest, lats, triceps and anterior chain return to the starting position. As you can see this exercise can be made rather easy or challenging depending on the height of the handles. Lower handles will provide the most challenge.

Step 2

A book bag is demonstrated as resistance tool in the photos above.

If using the USA it's not necessary because USA is designed for a quick change in resistance level.

Simply get a hold of one or two handles lower, and a new challenge is created.

Total Reach I Superman Pull

Step 3

Step three is the unilateral assisted movement. One arm does the movement and the other assists. Other methods can be used such as a partner or a resistance band. Make sure that your straight arm is under tension rather than simply flopping up and down while the other one pushes. In fact the USA can also be used for both push-ups and rows progression. This would call for mastery of bilateral variation at the lower handles first. Following that, the unilateral training can start with higher handles. With time and practice the hands can move down the USA. At the end, low handle unilateral variations will be perfected.

Step 4

Fourth step of the Superman Pull are negatives. Start in a slightly leaned forward position and lift one arm. Be prepared to step out and/or let go of your grip if you feel any sign of discomfort in your shoulder or the elbow. Progression from the higher handle at the beginning to the lower handle at the end will ensure minimum chance of injury as well.

Total Reach I Superman Pull

Step 5

This is the last step of unilateral superman pull mastery. Don't be fooled by the left arm. It holds the USA, while the right arm does the negative, but exerts no effort. It helps only slightly when the right arm pulls down.

Keep training this technique until no assistance is required to complete a full rep. At this point begin to practice with an aim of 2-3 reps. When this is achieved, go to a lower handle and repeat. With time you will progress to an awesome pull down power.

Be sure to checkout our Encyclopedia of Push-ups and Pull-ups.

This book takes a look at many innovative variations of both exercises. Many rarely seen variations are demonstrated. It also discusses proven and tested methods of developing strength, power in total movement as well as separate muscle groups. Several programs on top of developing high repetition sets are discussed. This is a must have for a serious fitness enthusiast.

Total Reach I Shoulder Flex

<u>Step 1</u>

Bilateral shoulder flex is the first step in this sequence. If you have never trained your shoulders in over head movement, you are up for a challenge.

This exercise is not easy even at the two armed stage. The goal is to articulate only one joint, the shoulder. The exercise begins with the trunk and legs on the slight incline and shoulders 45-90 degree bent. Using the strength of the deltoids, both arms are raised overhead to form a straight line with the trunk.

Don't be discouraged if this exercise seems too challenging at first. Go back and work on the Shoulder Press in the Heaven and Earth pair. That exercise will help to strengthen your muscles in the range required for the Shoulder Flex.

<u>Step 2</u>

Once the Shoulder Flex has been conquered, resisted training can begin.

The photos illustrate the use of a heavy object such as a book bag. You can simply get a hold of the lower handles and increase the resistance that way.

Total Reach I Shoulder Flex

<u>Step 3</u>

This is step three and assisted unilateral training is called for. In in the photos above, perform the Shoulder Flex with one arm while the other arms assists by performing a gentle rowing motion. If you want, use only two or one finger on the assisted hand. This may give you a clearer idea as to how much the non-training arm is helping the primary moving arm.

<u>Step 4</u>

This step is one arm negatives. To do this, use both arms to come up into the over head position. From there let go with one arm and fight gravity with the other.

Remember, this is a single joint exercise and the risk of injury increases. For this reason, make a serious effort in the previous three stages, prior to attempting the unassisted unilateral eccentric training.

Total Reach I Shoulder Flex

Step 5

Last step is here. Pat yourself on the back if you have made it this far. By now your shoulders can pack a good knock out punch.

First, decide which arm will be the prime mover. Use that arm ascend into the other hand position. Have the assistant arm help only as much as needed. On the way down use only the primary arm to lower yourself down. Repeat a few times, rest and repeat on the opposite side.

Core Transformation Book

This book is about functional core development. In most athletic or everyday movement the core serves as a stabilizer or a center for power transfer. This book discusses many ways of training the core for specific sport or everyday related functions. Many exercises don't even appear to have anything to do with mid-section, that is, until you try them. This book will open your eyes about the true nature of functional core training.

Total Reach II Superman Pull II

Step 1

This is the first exercise in Total Reach II Sequence. It is called Super Man Pull II.

The difference between Superman Pull I and II is that the latter calls for the adduction of the shoulder, while the former calls for the extension.

In other words, the arm is brought straight down in front of the body in the previous exercise. In this one the arm is lowered down to the side. It's similar to one arm Jumping Jack if you will. Notice that the palms of the both hands face toward each other at all times.

To start this exercise, place your body on a slight incline. Assuming that your right shoulder is lower, it will be your right arm which will execute the Superman Pull II. This arm should be extended out to the side. The grip on the apparatus should be palms up. The arm with the higher shoulder (left arm) will grip the apparatus a few handles higher. The left arm should extend in straight line with the trunk.

The goal is to articulate only at the shoulder joint. The trunk, hip and legs should be stabilized and maintained in one straight line. Lower yourself by moving your left arm away from your head , and right arm toward your head. Then reverse the movement and come back to the starting position.

Total Reach II Superman Pull II

Step 2

Second step is pretty much self explanatory. You can either add extra weight or use lower handles for added resistance. The basic technique remains the same.

Step 3

This is the third step. In this case the right arm does the movement and the left assists. Notice that the left hand is open. You can slide the fingers down the bar.

The farther away from the palm the handle is, the less assistance is provided by the left arm.

Total Reach II Superman Pull II

Step 4

Fourth step is the negatives. To do this use both hands to get into the top position and let go of the left hand. Use the right arm to lower yourself down into gravity.

Be prepared to step out and break your fall if it becomes necessary. Rest a while and try the other side.

Step 5

This is step five. If you are about to try this step, it means only one thing. You have mastered the one arm eccentric movement. If that is not the case, you will over use the assistance of the upper arm and won't get full benefits of this step.

Total Reach II Shoulder Over

Step 1

Now comes the second half of the Total Reach II. The Shoulder Over. The first step is the same as for the Superman Pull II. It is recommended to take the shoulder flex around the block, prior to taking on this challenge. The goal here is to add strength to the shoulder abductors in the upper range. In other words, the range of motion that this exercise develops is starting from the arm parallel to the floor to the arm straight over the head.

Step 2

Second step calls for additional resistance. Book bag is used in the photos above, but lower handles on USA or weighted vest can be used as well.

Make sure to hold the elbow in a fixed position. You do not want to bend the elbow too much when ascending. If you do, the bicep will be involved more than it should be. After all, this is a shoulder specific exercise.

Total Reach II Shoulder Over

Step 3

Step three is a unilateral movement with assistance. In this case the other arm helps out. An experienced partner can help out as well.

Having the assisting hand open can help to minimize its work. The closer the handles comes to the tip of the fingers, the more targeted arm is to rely on itself.

Step 4

This step is deltoid vs. gravity. At first the gravity will win, but after practice the deltoid will avenge itself. As always, master the upper handles before the lower.

This exercise is rather difficult and may at first seem impossible. Keep at it. Your muscles will always adapt as long as you give them time to heal and recuperate.

Total Reach II Shoulder Over

Step 5

By the time you get to this stage you'll be able to control the downward movement, but the positive is not going to be possible. In this case help yourself up. After a while, this help will no longer be needed.

Once again, the bottom hand is open, it's not gripping the rungs, this forces the top arm to carry its load. Stay with it, until the target arm can take over completely and unconditionally.

SECTION II - INTRODUCTION

The second section of this book focuses on the lower body exercises. In most cases, it's impossible to train the lower body without engaging the muscles of the midsection. At the same time, not all exercise are clearly geared to one muscle or the other. In some cases the performance of the exercise can shift the effort to one muscle group over the other.

For example, let's take a look at this step up. This is a very basic movement, during which you lift one leg up, place your foot on the chair or a step and extend the leg, propelling yourself up. The muscle groups used depends on the height of the chair, as well as, the dynamics of the body.

For instance, a low step such as a street curb doesn't force much of the bending forward of the trunk. This causes more stress to be placed on the quadriceps, rather than on the posterior chair (Gluteus Maximus and Hamstrings) On the other hand, a high chair often forces the forward lean and more posterior chain activation. Regardless of the cause, if you bend forward, the front of the leg will carry less work and the back of the leg will carry more. At the same time, the non stepping leg may engage its calve muscles to propel the movement.

As you can see, not everything is cut and dried. That being true, we will try to make an assumption that most exercises have more or less standard muscle recruitment. All the exercises in this section will be listed based on these recruitments.

The first chapter focuses on the exercises that tax the posterior chain. They include the Stiff Leg Dead Lift, Standing Back Kick Warrior III, Unilateral Hyperextension, and Unilateral Cobra Bends. The discussion will start with the explanation of the simplest moves and move on to more advanced techniques. One leg Stiff Leg Dead Lift is a classical example in functionality of the unilateral movement. It not only helps with strength it also helps with flexibility of the posterior chain. It is a very important extended length conditioning exercise found in ElasticSteel flexibility program. (See the back of the book for more information.)

This exercise can be developed using the classical power of one progression. Two legged variation, is followed by the close stance resisted or wide stance side to side variation. Next comes a one legged negative, followed by a non-assisted negative and an assisted positive. In most cases the above will not be necessary. Most people can do the one legged version after a few tries or after a short two legged preparation.

The standing back kick is a natural progression from the one leg dead lift. This exercise forces the posterior chain of the supporting leg to stabilize, while the other leg works. To do this exercise simply extend the suspended leg backward. The goal is to have the body and non-supportive leg completely parallel to the floor. The arms can be overhead in line with the body, or overhead.

The next exercise is Yoga's Warrior III this technique is somewhat more difficult than unilateral dead lift due to the fact that both the arms and the hands are extended when the trunk travels from 180 degree to 90 degrees and back. Customarily Warrior III is a static posture, but it can be made dynamic if you go into and out of it repeatedly.

The next exercise is unilateral hyper extension. This move is a relatively common exercise used to develop the posterior chain. Truth is it's rather uncommon for athletes in any sport or a hands on worker in any field to do something with both legs doing evenly distributed work at exactly the same time. One leg hyper extension are a lot more function, yet more challenging than a regular version.

The progression is similar to most other exercises. Start with two legged version until at least 20 good repetitions are mastered. Add weighted resistance. Practice the assisted one legged technique. Work on the negatives. As far as negatives you can use the other leg to help you up or you can use the arms to push up, prior to descending down with one leg.

Last step is unassisted negatives, combined with assisted positives. Concentric movement can be facilitated through the use of hands, other leg or a partner. Unilateral cobra bends is the only exercise that works the posterior chain, while the knee is in bent position. Other exercises in this section should be mastered prior to working on this technique. Once again the same exact progression down to mid-section exercises that is applied to hyperextensions can be utilized for the cobra bends.

SECTION 2
CHAPTER 1
Posterior Chain

One Leg Stiff Leg Dead Lift

One leg stiff leg dead lift is a very functional exercise for posterior chain. This unilateral variation is also a useful technique to develop dynamic balance. Most people don't need the Power of One progression to master this one leg exercise. However, if you have never done any posterior chain work or have never practiced a dead lift (bodyweight or otherwise) it makes sense to spend some time on the two legged version.

Simply stand on one leg and lean forward at the hip. Do not allow your back to bend. Once the body is parallel to the floor or as close a possible, reverse the movement and come back to the starting position. The hands can be kept behind the back as in the photos above; other options are over the head, behind the head, and hanging down as if you were to pick something off the floor.

Kick Back

Kick back is a natural progression from the unilateral stiff leg dead lift. This exercise is meant to be performed at the speed best accustomed to your activity. For someone who is not training for any sport, simple slow extension of the non-supported leg will do.

There are two ways to do this exercise. First is to flex at the hip like you would during a still leg dead lift. Then extend the non-weight bearing leg. Here, you can stay in bent over position and keep extending and retracting the other leg. Another option is to bend forward, kick back, retract the leg and stand up straight. This cycle can be repeated over and over again.

Just like with the stiff leg dead lift, the arms can be anywhere. The higher they move up the body the more challenging the exercise becomes. For example, hands behind the back variation is somewhat easier than arms extended over the head variation as seen in the next exercise, Warrior III.

Warrior III

Warrior III in a natural choice to progress to after practicing the previous two exercises. This is a yoga posture and is often taught as the static hold. For the purposes of this book, it can be treated as any other exercise.

Simply stand upright and extend your arms straight up, over your head. Lean forward keeping the arms, torso and non-weight bearing leg in one line. You will end up in the position above. You can stay there as long as you like or you can return to the starting position and repeat.

Unilateral Hyper Extension

Step 1

Unilateral Hyper Extension is a fun exercise. It's way more functional than bilateral dead lift. This bad boy is a jewel for any athlete, who runs, jumps, throws, kicks, punches etc.

As always, we start with bilateral training. This exercise requires a bench. In the photos above the athlete is held by his partner, because a hyperextension station is not available. It's possible to avoid a partner by using a strong strap or a weightlifting belt to tie your feet to the bench.

Make sure that the edge of the bench is under the hips. This ensures that the body can articulate from the hips and not from the spine.

Step 2

Weighted hyper extension is rather similar to the bodyweight one. This time a trainee holds a plate in his hands for added resistance. In reality the extra weight can be provided by any object. The hands are free and so almost anything can be held in them.

Unilateral Hyper Extension

Step 3

In this exercise, which is the assisted unilateral movement, a resistance band is the top choice. Second choice is the manual assistance by the performer. Notice only one leg is being held down, while the other is free.

Step 4

Step five calls for unassisted eccentric phase of the technique. Be prepared to use your hands to break a fall, in case your muscles can't hold you up. Use the other leg, to come back up. If you choose to do more than one negative in a row, simply ask your partner to hold on to both ankles when you return to the starting position.

If a break must be taken between attempts, just get off the bench for as long as needed and then return to try again.

Unilateral Hyper Extension

Step 5

The last stage starts with upward motion supported by the resistance band.

Once at the top, bands are no longer needed and the negative half of the exercise is assistance free.

Second partner, if available can help to ascend as well.

Cobra Bends

Step 1

Cobra bends provide a unique opportunity to train the posterior chain to its max. Start this exercise by kneeling. Attach your feet to the bench or anchor them under a stable, heavy object. Your partner can also hold down your feet as seen in the photos above. Bend forward from the hips. The photos above demonstrate the lower hip position at 90 degrees. You can go passed that if you choose. At the same time, the knees can be kept at a 90 degree angle throughout the exercise. You can choose to vary the knee angle as well, as seen above.

Step 2

Second step of Power of One progression to unilateral cobra bends involves adding extra resistance. Weighted vest, weighted book bag, is great if you have it. In case you don't, don't worry. You can use dumbbells, barbells, plates, etc., instead. The technique is exactly the same as for the first step. Be prepared for natural compensation of your body for extra resistance. There will be a tendency to shift the hips backward to compensate for the extra weight in the front of the body. If this is the case, and you can't reverse it and keep your hips over your knees, this means the chosen weight is too heavy for you. Lighten up on the extra load and try again.

Cobra Bends

Step 3

Elastic bands are very useful for the third step of unilateral cobra bends progression. All you have to do is find a bar over head to which the bands can attached too. Grab the band with both hands, have your partner hold one foot and go. If the bands are not readily available, you can substitute for them with manual assistance. In this case you will have to find an object, which you can push up against when you execute the cobra

bend. Remember to always give yourself a short break before switching over to the other side. That's because the glutes and hams will be used on the other leg, but the core won't have a complete substitution and need a bit more rest.

Step 4

Here come the negatives. Be ready to break the fall with your hands, in case you loose control and you begin to plummet down head first. Also protect yourself at all times. If for whatever reason your partner lets go, or the device holding your feet breaks loose, you don't want to head butt the floor. So keep your hands ready for action.

Cobra Bends

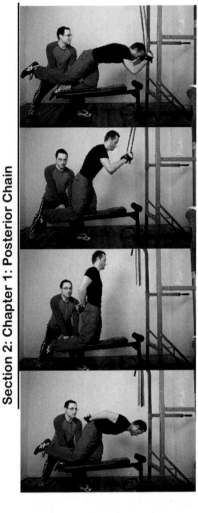

This is the last step before the technique is mastered. Use the resistance band to come up. Once you are in a vertical position, let go off the band. Lean forward and descend with control.

Position the assistance mechanism in such a way, that it will allow you to use it right after the negative. For example, in the photo the resistance band can't be used to assist in the positive movement. It's too short. The athlete would not be able to grasp it. If it were longer, hanging slightly below his head, it would have been in the right position to assist the concentric motion.

SECTION 2
CHAPTER 2
Compound Leg Exercises

This section deals with the exercises utilizing both the front and back of the leg. In addition the inside and outside of the thigh provide support.

The first exercise in this section is a Step Up. Although this exercise is considered "too easy" by most, it is an important one leg technique that can be trained without any special transfer protocol. The step up and it's cousin, side step up are both good preparatory techniques that are coming up in this section.

One Leg Dead Lift has a similar sounding name to One Leg Stiff Dead Lift, but movement-wise there is a difference. A regular one legged dead lift allows for the flexion and extension of the knee, thus recruiting the quadriceps into the action. Most people who can do a stiff leg dead lift, would be able to master the regular unilateral dead lift in a relatively short time. Some effort will be necessary due to obvious difference in movement. To master this exercise retrace the five steps of Power of One program.

The next exercise is more quadriceps dominated exercise, although other muscle groups are still in use. It's what is some times referred to as the king of leg exercises, the one leg squat. One leg squat is one of 12 maximum resistance exercises in the Gravity Advantage Max book. In that book a different path is outlined to master the one leg squat. Take a look at GAM if you are interested in that path. For the purpose of this book the five classical Power of One step will get you to be the king of leg exercises.

The last exercise in this program is the Warrior Press. If one leg squat is the king, this exercise must be the emperor, for its more difficult than the other members of the leg strength nobility. The difference between the press and a squat, is that the former must be performed while the body is parallel to the floor.

At the same time at the bottom of the technique the body is balanced only on its toes. For this reason every major muscle in the lower body must make a coordinated effort to master this royal technique. The training of the Warrior Press resembles the training similar to any other technique.

However, it is recommended that one leg squat and one leg toe press are mastered first. For One Leg Toe Press exerciese, please see the lower leg section of the book.

Step Up

Step up is a simple, yet effective unilateral leg exercise. Most people don't have difficulty in performing this exercise. If it so happens that you do, the situation is easily correctable.

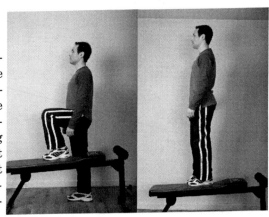

Simply use a low step and increase the height as you get more adept.

Basic step up has two variations. You can ascend the bench by facing it or by standing sideways to it. The exercise shown here is the side step up. The front step up would be the same technique except the athlete would face the camera, while the bench remains unmoved.

It is possible that you will do 20 step ups right away. If that's the case, consider adding resistance to this exercise.

*Bi*lateral Bodyweight Dead Lift

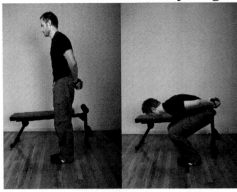

Step 1

This is the first step in mastering the unilateral dead lift. Bodyweight dead lift is an oxymoron to most people. After all when you dead lift aren't you supposed to dead lift something? Although it's true, a bodyweight version can be trained as well. Think of it this way; Once you master the single leg dead lift, you would be able to add weight to it. This will be a pretty functional exercise.

The picture above demonstrates the most common mistakes when performing the dead lift. Please compare the photos on this page with the photos on the next page illustrating the weighted dead lift.

1. You want to be looking ahead and not down.
2. You want to keep your spine straight and not curved.
3. You want your back to bend only as much as necessary for the hands to reach the floor.
4. When you stand up you want to be in straight, vertical line from head to feet.

Step 2

This is the weighted variation as required for the level two of Power of One program. The weighted book bag is used. You don't have to go out and get yourself a spare book bag, if you don't have one al-

ready. Dumbbells and barbell will do as well.

---

*Bi*lateral Bodyweight Dead Lift

Step 3

Here is the assisted version. A resistance band it used, while each leg learns to handle the whole weight of the body. The band goes in front of the chest and under the arms. On the top it is fixed to the power station. You can also use a pair of chairs. Place each chair on either side of you and dead lift away.

Step 4

This is the fourth step. From standing position, descend into the dead lift using only one leg. Use the other leg to come back up.

*Bi*lateral Bodyweight Dead Lift

<u>Step 5</u>

The last step of a regular Power of One program is often not needed for this exercise. In other words, unilateral negative and assisted positive are often bypassed. Most people tend to learn how to come back up after a few negatives. In case you are having difficulty, you can simply descend with one leg and then ascend with the only a slight help of the other leg. Another option would be to use the chairs when coming up, but not when going down.

Latest Online Courses Offered by Paul Zaichik

Kicking Technique in Depth

This course teaches absolutely everything one needs to know to develop super sharp kicking techniques. Tests are demonstrated to find out the weak link of your techniques and fix it. Special exercises are taught to improve every area of the kicks. Main focus is on speed, power, endurance, precision, focus, height, control, and timing. This ONLINE COURSE is taught by Paul Zaichik. This is a 12 weeks course which consists of follow along classes, presented to the trainee every week. Here you will have the opportunity to showcase your progress to Paul Zaichik and get his feedback on your progress.

Bodyweight Squat

Step 2

This is the second step of the squat progression. Don't worry, you didn't miss the first step. The first step is exactly the same as in the photos above, only without the book bag.

Three things to keep in mind:
1. Look straight ahead.
2. Keep your back in a straight line.
3. Feet flat. There is a tendency to get the heals off the floor but you should keep the heels in contact with the floor.

Notice: The hips are only lowered to the height of the knees and the descend ends when your thigh is parallel to the floor. This is an option, not a rule. If you are an advanced squatter, and feel comfortable coming down lower, please by all means do so.

Step 3

Step three is the assisted one leg squat. Resistance band is your friend. It can help you or it can make your moves more difficult. Here the band does a good job assisting the unilateral movement. Don't worry, if the band is

not present. Assisted one leg squats look just as good with a little help from the hands, holding on to anything sturdy. Here is an interesting note. This is the first time you have to keep the other leg straight and lifted. What you may experience. The squatting leg will do it's job, but the other leg may fail. You may simply not have enough strength or flexibility to hold the straight leg up. A simple solution will be to stand on something 6 or more inches higher than the floor. This will allow the straight leg to be less elevated.

Bodyweight Squat

Step 4

One leg negative squats are a bit tricky. If you have never done them, you may find balance more of a problem than strength. You way want to practice them next to a way, in case a slight miscalculation of balance will send you fly-

ing. Once descended, use the other leg to come back up.

Step 5

Here the bands are used to come up, but not to come down. Notice that the bands is not in the best position. If its assistance is need to get up, it will be hard to get a hold of it. Having the band in front is usually a better idea. Your other leg, wall, rope and other devices can help on the positive phase of the exercise as well.

Leg Press

Step 1

If you are ready for the emperor of the leg exercises here comes the Warrior Press. This is a true power move. Its two legged variation is called a Bodyweight Leg Press.

First and foremost, here are a couple of things you need to know before attempting the progression to the emperor:

1. You need flexibility in the posterior chain. If you can't at least touch the floor with your hands, while the knee are straight, you should not attempt this move. You need to master these seven moves first:

   - One Leg Dead Lift.
   - One Leg Squat
   - One Leg Stiff Legged Dead Lift.
   - Warrior III
   - Single Leg Press
   - Single Leg Warrior Toe Press
   - Beggar's Knees (optional)

2. You must have no current knee injuries.
3. You must have patience.

If you're curious as to why there are so many pre-requisites, you will soon find out.

The leg press starts out in a bow position. Here the legs are straight and the torso is strait and parallel to the floor. With torso in the same position, bend the legs and lower yourself. Reverse the movement and come back to the starting position.

Leg Press

Step 2

Graduating from the bodyweight leg press, we now move on to the weighted leg press. In this step, we use resistance, by placing it on the lower back. Safety and biomechanics both dictate for this placement of the weight.

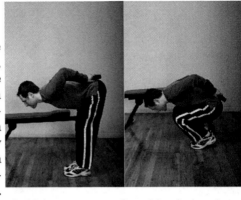

While a heavy bag is probably a more comfortable choice, iron plate is used to demonstrate that it too can be a valuable tool. If you like to work with a partner, you can have him sit on your pelvis. It would be best for him to hold on to something that he can pull up against, thus regulating the amount of load you have to carry. You in turn can use your hand to secure your partner in place.

Step 3

Here you can see an idea for assisted unilateral movement. Just as one leg squat, the Warrior Press can be assisted by using one or both arms. If your heart's set on resistance bands, by all means go for it and use it as your trusted helper.

Leg Press

Step 4

Master the assisted warrior press and you are ready for the negative training. The picture above shows the lowest that one can go while keeping the other leg bent. If the other leg was to be extended straight back, a bit more range of motion will be possible.

It's a good idea to keep the bench nearby, just in case the balance escapes you. Pay close attention to your knees. If they give you a signal that's not a good one, stop what you doing right away. Evaluate what your body is trying to tell you. Few reps in the heat of the moment is not worth an injury. Remember ; this is an advanced technique, which has many pre-requisites.

Step 5

Warrior Press is no different than other exercises. Follow the Power of One progression, be patient and you will master it. As you can see in the photos above, the arm is used to help to extend the leg, while no assistance is provided on the descent. This exercise can make a champion, but only if you give it respect. It is royalty, and for a very valid reason.

SECTION 2
CHAPTER 3
Anterior Chain & Quadriceps

The next section of this book presents two anterior chain and quadriceps specific exercises. The first exercise is called a Slow Front Kick. Notice, this is not a front kick, it's a slow front kick. This exercise looks simple, but when performed with control, in an unhurried fashion, it forces even the best athletes to shake. Unlike other techniques slow front kick requires no progression. All you have to do is practice this technique. If you have limited flexibility and would like to increase the height of the kick please see ElasticsSteel flexibility products at elasticsteel.net.

The second exercise is called a beggar's knees. This is a primary knee extensors training technique. To master it start with bilateral variation and trace the Power of One 5 step progression. Unlike other exercises, it is recommended to master upward of 40 one legged variations prior to moving on to the next step. You must be very careful to pay attention to traction of the knee. Make sure that the knees don't go too much in or out and bend naturally. Avoid this exercise if knee pain is present.

This is a basic front kick. Since its purpose in this book is not for combat, this technique has a very simple delivery. Begin by lifting the knee of the kicking leg. While balancing on one leg, extend the lifted leg slowly. Recover to the starting position. Do as many as possible, prior to placing the knee back down. If you find that you can't extend the leg, that means that the knee has to be lower and the kicking foot must extend to lower height. You don't have to be a fighter to practice this kick. It is a very beneficial unilateral training technique. In this book the primary reason to practice this kick is to develop the quadriceps and the hip flexors. Besides those benefits, the front kick also develops a sense of balance, as well as core and glute muscles.

Beggar's Knees

Step 1

Beggar's knees is a quadriceps specific technique. Start this exercise by facing the wall. Place both hands on the wall. Move your feet back approximately a foot. Your feet should be behind and not under your shoulders. Slowly, with control lower your knees to the floor. Using the strength of your quadriceps, press back up to the starting position. Just like basic squats, most people can do a bilateral variation, but one leg at a time poses a challenge.

Step 2

Weighted Beggar's knees uses exactly the same technique as the resistance-free variation. Real weight seems to be most useful here. Back pack, weighted vest and the like are a more comfortable form of resistance, than resistance band or partner pressure.

Beggar's Knees

Step 3

Assisted unilateral training is shown on the photos above. Resistance tube is employed for upward assistance. The non training leg is simply flexed at the knee. It provides no assistance to the movement.

Negative exercise would be next (Step 4). This exercise is not demonstrated, only explained. To do this step stand with both legs in the starting position. Lift one leg and slowly bring the knee of the other leg to the ground. Use a pillow under the knee, if there is a chance that your control can be lost and an injury can be received.

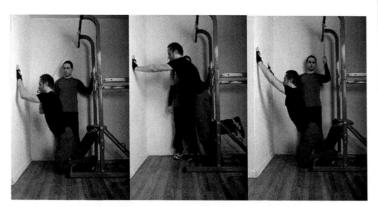

Notice: This is the fifth step. The fourth step is not demonstrated, only explained, following the explanation of the third step.

Here we see a partner give a resistance tube to the trainee. Once the trainee gets the tube, he rises using the elastic assistance. Once the assisted positive part of the exercise is completed, he then lets go of the tube and comes back down without assistance.

SECTION 2
CHAPTER 4
Lower Leg Exercises

The next part of this section concentrates on the lower leg. Just think of how often an athlete twists an ankle or falls down while in the middle of the game. Most of this has to do with non-function bilateral toe presses and other equally distributed exercises that don't transfer to athletics. Out of all lower leg exercises only a few need a progression sequence. Most others can be picked up easily on the spot. The fact is they are so functional that they must be included in this book.

The two most challenging exercises in this section demand mastery of strength and balance. They are the single leg toe press and the single leg warrior toe press.

Each of the techniques can be mastered through the five step progression sequence. The warrior toe press does require the mastery of the warrior III position, before advancing into the toe press variation. In most cases the mastery of the warrior press and warrior III will lead to an easy gain of the combination of them.

The other three exercises are single leg hops. These moves closely resemble athletic biomechanics of the lower leg. Two techniques are recommended as pre-requisites of single leg hops, the double leg hops and unilateral toe presses. It only makes sense that bilateral movement must precede the unilateral and strength conditioning and must come before plyometric application. The double leg hop, which is not illustrated in this book, is simply jumping in 8 directions using both legs.

The first one leg hop exercise calls for 8 directional hops. Simply stand on one leg and jump forward, back, left, right. Then repeat the 4 jumps, this time front right, back left, front left, back right. Once you are comfortable with it, you can start jumping over an object placed in the center. This way you have to jump over it every time you hop.

The next exercise is one leg hop and turn. A jump with a 90 degree turn in either direction will do. As you get more advanced 180 degree and 360 degrees will provide more challenge. Jumping in 8 directions and spinning at the same time is an even more complex training technique.

Unilateral Bodyweight Toe Press

Unilateral bodyweight toe press is an easily attainable technique. In fact most people can do it without progressing to it. After all, this movement is very natural to us. You simply stand on one leg and go up on your toes. The

issue is repetitions. Most of us can do a few reps, but won't be able to do say, 30. Another way to challenge yourself with this technique is to hold yourself in the top position, only supported by your toes. This exercise is pretty functional especially for athletes who take interest in jumping, balance and agility. It is also a pre-requisite for the other lower leg exercises coming up next.

Single Leg Warrior Toe Press

This is the single leg warrior toe press. Same lower leg movement as in the previous exercise. The torso however stays parallel to the floor throughout the exercise. Two variations are shown above. One variation calls for the non-exercise leg to be only flexed at the knee. The second and slightly more difficult variation calls for body and non-weight bearing leg to be in line with the floor.

One Leg Hop

This is a one leg hop. The same one children incorporate in their play on the sidewalk. Just like a jump rope, it's more than a child's way to be entertained. If you think otherwise, please try this for few minutes and see what happens.

The photos above demonstrate a basic circular pattern. There are two thick lines on the floor. The goal is to jump forward, left, back, and right. Feel free to make up your own patters. You can jump forward and back, left and right and on the angles.

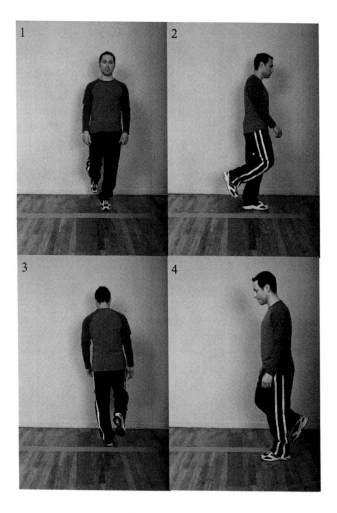

One Leg Hop

The photos above add a turn to the challenge. A hop with a 90 degree turn is shown on picture 1 and 2, bottom two pictures 3 and 4 show a hop to the side with a 90 degree turn. Use your imagination to create a more fun variation. A turn can be any number of degrees. While a simultaneous hop can be in any direction. You can also have your partner call out degrees and directions at random.

SECTION 2
CHAPTER 5
Hip Flexors & Abdominals

The last chapter deals with hip flexors and abdominals. An exercise presented here is a good opponent technique to posterior chain moves. This exercise is called the One Leg Sit Up. If used together with glute and hamstrings exercises, the one leg sit up should be done last.

The progression for this technique is the same as for others utilizing the Power of One program. The good part, is that any weight can be held in your hands while working on second step of the program.

The photographs in the next few pages demonstrate the straight hip sit up. This is a more functional variation for most sports then a common flexed hip sit up. We recommend to go with your trainers recommendation. You can substitute all the exercises to make it a flexed hip sit ups simply by bending your knee and hooking your foot under the stable object.

If it so happens that you nailed the one leg sit up the first time you tried it, there are four variation that will keep you challenged. Those include the twist, the leg up, the leg over and the leg out variations. Moreover you can change the inclination of the bench. A high decline one legged sit up is one of the finest hip flexor conditioning exercises bodyweight training has to offer.

If you think the challenge stops here. Guess what, it doesn't. Many of those variations can be combined. Take a decline, leg out, sit up with a twist for example. That should be enough to keep you busy for a very long time.

Enjoy the training that will make you a champion!

Sit Up

Step 1

This is the first step in mastering the unilateral sit-up. You simply have to be able to do at least 20 good bodyweight sit ups. The technique demonstrated above calls for a straight line from knee to shoulder at the start of the exercise. This is not standard way for performing sit-ups. Most people are taught to do sit ups with knees and hips flexed. You should perform them as your instructor demonstrates it. Make sure to keep your abdominals tensed at all times regardless of the technique used.

Step 2

In the second step a weighted object is placed on the chest. If you choose to use a book bag, make sure to wear it in the front.

Sit Up

Step 3

The resistance band is perfect aid to this exercise providing that you have something to attach the band to. In order to work only one leg at the time, simply place one leg over the ankle bar, while the other under the ankle bar.

Step 4

This step is a negative movement. This is rather simple. Use one leg to come down and both legs to come up. You can also use your hands to come up. Remember, this step calls for a short rest before another negative is attempted.

Sit Up

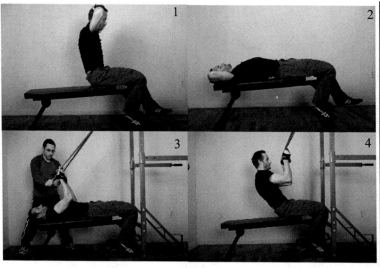

Step 5

Unlike step four where every negative is surrounded by rest, step five mixes them up, non-stop. Photos above demonstrate unassisted negative and resistance band assisted positive. Notice, a partner gives the band to the trainee to use it for the positive phase of the movement. Another option would be to use the other leg to come up. If you choose to do this, minimize the assistance provided by the other leg.

Bodyweight Training in Depth

Be sure to visit www.ElasticSteel.net for more information about this one of a kind ONLINE TRAINING COURSE brought to you by Paul Zaichik.

This course covers every part of your body and shows you how bodyweight training can target any specific muscle group or a needed movement. The world of bodyweight training is taken out of contest of few popular exercises such as dips and crunches and explored through it's full spectrum. A person walking away form this course will know how to train for any specific goal using only his or her own weight.

Unilateral Sit Up Variations

Here are some variations that you can add to one leg sit up to make it more challenging. Pictures 1,2 and 3 demonstrate the rotation combined with main movement. Pictures 4,5 and 6 demonstrate leg up, leg over, and leg out variation respectively.

Leg up variation simply calls for the non-training leg to be lifted as high as possible. Leg over variation is performed by placing the other leg over the knee of the primary moving leg. Last but not least the leg out variation requires the non-training leg to be lifted straight out to the sides and to remain there throughout the set. Each of these poses a separate challenge in it's own way.

Feel free to place the bench on the decline, this will be a host of new challenges. If it so happens that you easily topped all the variations, extra weight is the next option. For example, a decline, unilateral, leg out sit up with a twist, while holding a 45 lbs plate in your hands. Have fun and be safe training, that's the most important thing!

STRENGTH EXERCISES RECOMMENDATIONS FOR VARIOUS SPORTS

Check with your coach for instructions on how to incorporate the exercises below into your training regiment. Your instructor may recommend variations of the exercises for your specific needs.

Grappling/Wrestling

- Routine 1: Double Up, Dead lift, Warrior Press, Unilateral Sit Up
- Routine 2: Total Control I and Total Control II, Unilateral Hyper extensions, Unilateral Sit Up
- Routine 3: Heaven and Earth, Beggar Knees, Cobra, 8D, Unilateral Sit Up

Boxing

- Routine 1: Plyometric Ying Yang, Step up with jump, toe press
- Program 2: Beast master or Great effort, dead lift, 8D hops, one leg sit up
- Program 3: Total reach 1 or 2 one leg squat, 8D hops
- Program 4: Total Control, Warrior toe presses, one leg sit up with a twist

Pitching Baseball/Softball

- Program 1: Step Up, Yin Yang, Toe Press
- Program 2: One leg dead lift, total reach I, One leg sit up with a twist

Hand Ball

- Program 1: Side Step Up, Plyometric Yin Yang, Toe Press
- Program 2: Dead Lift, Total Reach I, 8D Hops in crouched position

Tennis

- Program 1: Side Step Up, Great Effort, Toe Press
- Program 2: Dead Lift, Total Reach, 8D and turns

Foot Ball (Line Backer)

- Program1: Dead Lift, great effort, toe press
- Program 2: One leg Squat, Beast Master, Warrior Toe Press

Foot Ball (Quarter Back)

- Program 1: Step Up, Yin Yang, Toe Press
- Program 2: One leg dead lift, total reach I, One leg sit up with a twist

Cross County Running

- Program 1: Step Up, Front Kick, Toe press
- Program 2: Side Step up, Stiff leg dead lift, 8D
- Program 3: One leg Squat, Warrior Toe press

Baseball

- Program 1: Step Up, Great effort, One leg toe press
- Program 2: Dead Lift, Yin Yang (the pushup part can be with the hand on the ball), 8D
- Program 3: One Leg Squat, Double Up (Even two arms is very help full), 8D over basket ball

Hockey

- Program 1: Side Step up, Ying Yang, 8D
- Program 2: Hindu Pushup, Bridge Row, One leg dead lift, 8D with 90 or 180 degree turns
- Program 3: Total control 2, unilateral hyper extensions, unilateral sit up

Soccer

- Program 1: Slow front kick, stiff leg dead lift, Yin Yang
- Program 2: One leg squat, 8D, Ying Yang
- Program 3: Warrior presses, one leg squat, one leg sit up

Dear Reader,

The second edition of this book is currently in the works and will include more exercises, more photos, illustrations and programs. It will also address all the needs and questions that you may have.

Please post all your questions and comments to the following sites:

ElasticSteel.net
&
BodyWeightCulture.com

You can also send us an email to guys@bwculture.net, admin@bodyweightculture.com or sales@elasticsteel.com.

If you liked this book and want to see a second edition which will include answer to all of your concerns, we ask you to help spread the word about this book, tell your friends and family, coworkers, acquaintances and anyone you feel would benefit from this book. The more people get the knowledge in these pages the better.

Remember, without your help in spreading the word about The Power of One, a second edition will not be possible.

Once again we'd love to hear your thoughts on this book, so don't be shy and post to our sites so that we can better understand & address your needs.

Best Regards,

Paul Zaichik
&
GUYS @ BWC

Notes

Notes